Me and
My Nan

First published in 2009
by Wayland

This paperback edition published in 2010 by Wayland

Text copyright © Amanda Rainger 2009
Illustration copyright © Simone Abel 2009

Wayland
338 Euston Road
London NW1 3BH

Wayland Australia
Level 17/207 Kent Street
Sydney, NSW 2000

Series Editor: Louise John
Cover design: Paul Cherrill
Design: D.R.ink
Consultant: Shirley Bickler

A CIP catalogue record for this book is available from the British Library.

ISBN 9780750258104 (hbk)
ISBN 9780750260268 (pbk)

Printed in China

Wayland is a division of Hachette Children's Books,
an Hachette UK Company

www.hachette.co.uk

Me and My Nan

Written by Amanda Rainger
Illustrated by Simone Abel

WAYLAND

Nan came to meet me
to take me to her flat.

I ran on to the bus stop.
Nan said, "Don't do that!"

We went to the shops,
and Nan stopped for a chat.

I hid round the corner.
Nan said, "Don't do that!"

We walked by the river
and I shouted, "There's a rat!"

I thought it was funny.
Nan said, "Don't do that!"

I knocked on the front door with a rat-a-tat-tat!

Nan dropped all the shopping.
She said, "Don't do that!"

We had ham for tea,
but I don't like the fat.

So I hid it in the plant pot.
Nan said, "Don't do that!"

I dropped the ketchup.
It landed, ker-splat!

Nan spilt her tea.
She said, "Don't do that!"

Nan watched the TV.
I played with the cat.

He ran up the curtains.
Nan said, "Don't do that!"

I went into the bedroom,
and tried on Nan's hat.

It made me giggle.
Nan said, "Don't do that!"

I went into the garden,
with my ball and my bat,

but I stood on the flowers.
Nan said, "Don't do that!"

So I got out my book,
and I sat on the mat.

I tried to be good.
Nan said, "Yes! Do that!"

START READING is a series of highly enjoyable books for beginner readers. **The books have been carefully graded to match the Book Bands widely used in schools.** This enables readers to be sure they choose books that match their own reading ability.

Look out for the Band colour on the book in our Start Reading logo.

The Bands are:

Pink Band 1A & 1B

Red Band 2

Yellow Band 3

Blue Band 4

Green Band 5

Orange Band 6

Turquoise Band 7

Purple Band 8

Gold Band 9

START READING books can be read independently or shared with an adult. They promote the enjoyment of reading through satisfying stories supported by fun illustrations.

Amanda Rainger writes books and TV programmes for children learning French and Spanish. Best of all, she likes making up songs and stories — especially in rhyme! She works in a shed in the garden, with a tortoise, a fox and a chaffinch for company.

Simone Abel has illustrated over 200 books for children and has even won some awards. Best of all, she likes drawing people and animals, although she has just finished illustrating a book about cakes, which was great fun! She lives in Yorkshire, with her husband who is a painter, and their two daughters.